Treble Clef Brass
Scales & Exercises

for Trinity Guildhall examinations from 2007

Grades 1-8

Published by:
Trinity College London
89 Albert Embankment
London SE1 7TP UK

T +44 (0)20 7820 6100
F +44 (0)20 7820 6161
E music@trinityguildhall.co.uk
www.trinityguildhall.co.uk

Printed in England by Halstan & Co. Ltd, Amersham, Bucks.

Grade 1

Candidate to prepare one lip flexibility exercise and then *either* Section i) *or* Section ii) in full:

Lip Flexibility Exercise:

No. 1 Ascending and descending

♩ = c. 86   Play this exercise slurred, using the valve combinations given.

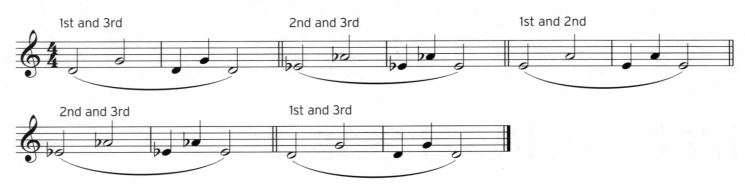

or

No. 2 Descending and ascending

♩ = c. 86   Play this exercise slurred, using the valve combinations given.

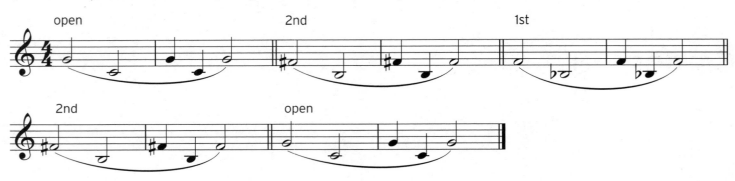

either i) **Scales and Arpeggios (from memory):**

The following scales and arpeggios to be performed *mf* and tongued (♩ = 46-60):

C major scale (one octave)

C major arpeggio (one octave)

A natural minor scale (one octave)

Alternatively, candidates may play the harmonic *or* melodic form of the minor, as follows:

A harmonic minor scale (one octave)

or

A melodic minor scale (one octave)

A minor arpeggio (one octave)

or ii) **Exercise:**

The following exercise to be performed tongued (♩ = 46–60):

C major scale and arpeggio exercise

Grade 2

Candidate to prepare one lip flexibility exercise and then *either* Section i) *or* Section ii) in full:

Lip Flexibility Exercise:

No. 1 Ascending and descending

♩ = *c.* 92   Play this exercise slurred, using the valve combinations given.

or

No. 2 Descending and ascending

♩ = *c.* 80   Play this exercise slurred, using the valve combinations given.

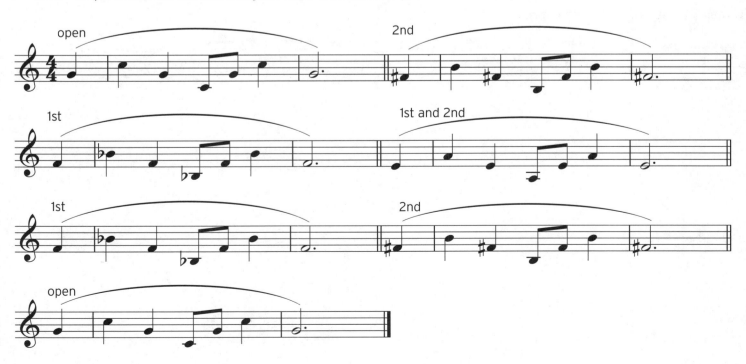

either i) **Scales and Arpeggios (from memory):**

The following scales and arpeggios to be performed *mf* and tongued *or* slurred as requested by the examiner (♩ = 50-66):

D major scale (one octave)

D major arpeggio (one octave)

A harmonic minor scale (one octave)

Alternatively, candidates may play the natural *or* melodic form of the minor, as follows:

A natural minor scale (one octave)

or

A melodic minor scale (one octave)

A minor arpeggio (one octave)

B♭ major scale (one octave)

B♭ major arpeggio (one octave)

Grade 2 continued

or ii) **Exercises:**

The following exercises to be performed *either* tongued *or* including slurs as indicated, as requested by the examiner
(♩ = 50-66):

D major scale and arpeggio exercise

A minor scale and arpeggio exercise

Grade 3

Candidate to prepare one lip flexibility exercise and then *either* Section i) *or* Section ii) in full:

Lip Flexibility Exercise:

No. 1 Ascending and descending

♩ = c. 92   Play this exercise slurred, using the valve combinations given.

or

No. 2 Descending and ascending

♩= c. 92   Play this exercise slurred, using the valve combinations given.

Grade 3 continued

either i) **Scales and Arpeggios (from memory):**

The following scales and arpeggios to be performed *mf* and tongued *or* slurred as requested by the examiner (♩ = 54-72):

C harmonic minor scale (one octave)

or

C melodic minor scale (one octave)

C minor arpeggio (one octave)

Whole-tone scale starting on C (one octave)

Eb major scale (one octave)

Eb major arpeggio (one octave)

E major scale (one octave)

E major arpeggio (one octave)

E harmonic minor scale (one octave)

or

E melodic minor scale (one octave)

E minor arpeggio (one octave)

or ii) **Exercises:**

The following exercises to be performed *either* tongued *or* including slurs as indicated, as requested by the examiner (♩ = 54-72):

C minor scale and arpeggio exercise

E♭ major scale and arpeggio exercise

E major scale and arpeggio exercise

Grade 4

Candidate to prepare one lip flexibility exercise and then *either* Section i) *or* Section ii) in full:

Lip Flexibility Exercise:

No. 1 Ascending and descending

♩ = c. 92   Play this exercise slurred, using the valve combinations given.

Repeat using the following valve combinations:

1st − 2nd − open − 2nd − 1st − 1st and 2nd

or

No. 2 Descending and ascending

♩ = c. 92   Play this exercise slurred, using the valve combinations given.

Repeat using the following valve combinations:

2nd − 1st − 1st and 2nd − 1st − 2nd − open

either i) **Scales and Arpeggios (from memory):**

The following scales and arpeggios to be performed ***mf*** and tongued *or* slurred as requested by the examiner (♩ = 60-104):

Chromatic scale starting on C (one octave)

D harmonic minor scale (one octave)

or

D melodic minor scale (one octave)

D minor arpeggio (one octave)

F major scale (one octave)

F major arpeggio (one octave)

F harmonic minor scale (one octave)

or

F melodic minor scale (one octave)

F minor arpeggio (one octave)

Whole-tone scale starting on F (one octave)

B♭ major scale (to 12th)

B♭ major arpeggio (to 12th)

Grade 4 continued

or ii) **Exercises:**

The following exercises to be performed *either* tongued *or* including slurs as indicated, as requested by the examiner
(♩ = 60-104):

F major expanding scale exercise

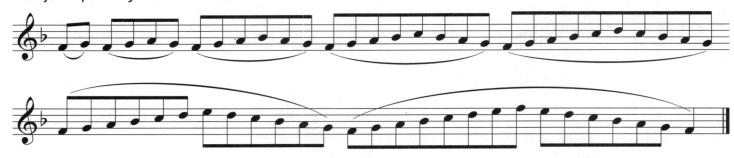

F minor expanding scale exercise

B♭ major scale and arpeggio exercise

Grade 5

Candidate to prepare one lip flexibility exercise and then *either* Section i) *or* Section ii) in full:

Lip Flexibility Exercise:

No. 1 Ascending

♩ = c. 120   Play this exercise slurred, using the valve combinations given.

1st and 3rd

Repeat using the following valve combinations:

2nd and 3rd – 1st and 2nd – 1st – 2nd – open

or

No. 2 Descending

♩ = c. 120   Play this exercise slurred, using the valve combinations given.

open

Repeat using the following valve combinations:

2nd – 1st – 1st and 2nd – 2nd and 3rd – 1st and 3rd

either i) **Scales and Arpeggios (from memory):**

The following scales and arpeggios to be performed *mf* and tongued *or* slurred as requested by the examiner (♩ = 60-104):

G major scale (two octaves)

G major arpeggio (two octaves)

Grade 5 continued

G harmonic minor scale (two octaves)

or

G melodic minor scale (two octaves)

G minor arpeggio (two octaves)

Chromatic scale starting on G (two octaves)

Whole-tone scale starting on G (two octaves)

Dominant 7th in the key of G (one octave)*

*If preferred, the dominant 7th may be finished on the starting note rather than resolving onto the tonic.

B major scale (to 12th)

B major arpeggio (to 12th)

B harmonic minor scale (to 12th)

or

B melodic minor scale (to 12th)

B minor arpeggio (to 12th)

or ii) **Exercises:**

The following exercises to be performed *either* tongued *or* including slurs as indicated, as requested by the examiner (♩ = 66–112):

B major scale and arpeggio exercise

Grade 5 continued

B minor scale and arpeggio exercise

G major expanding scale exercise

G minor expanding scale exercise

Grade 6

Candidate to prepare one lip flexibility exercise and then *either* Section i) *or* Section ii) in full:

Lip Flexibility Exercise:

No. 1 Ascending

♩ = c. 160   Play this exercise slurred, using the valve combinations given.

1st and 3rd

Repeat using the following valve combinations:

2nd and 3rd – 1st and 2nd – 1st – 2nd – open

or

No. 2 Descending

♩ = c. 60   Play this exercise slurred, using the valve combinations given.

open

Repeat using the following valve combinations:

2nd – 1st – 1st and 2nd – 2nd and 3rd – 1st and 3rd

either i) **Scales and Arpeggios (from memory):**

The following scales and arpeggios to be performed $\boldsymbol{f}$ *or* $\boldsymbol{p}$, tongued *or* slurred *or* staccato tongued as requested by the examiner (♩ = 72–120):

F# major scale (two octaves)

F# major arpeggio (two octaves)

Grade 6 continued

F# harmonic minor scale (two octaves)

F# melodic minor scale (two octaves)

F# minor arpeggio (two octaves)

A major scale (two octaves)

A major arpeggio (two octaves)

A harmonic minor scale (two octaves)

A melodic minor scale (two octaves)

A minor arpeggio (two octaves)

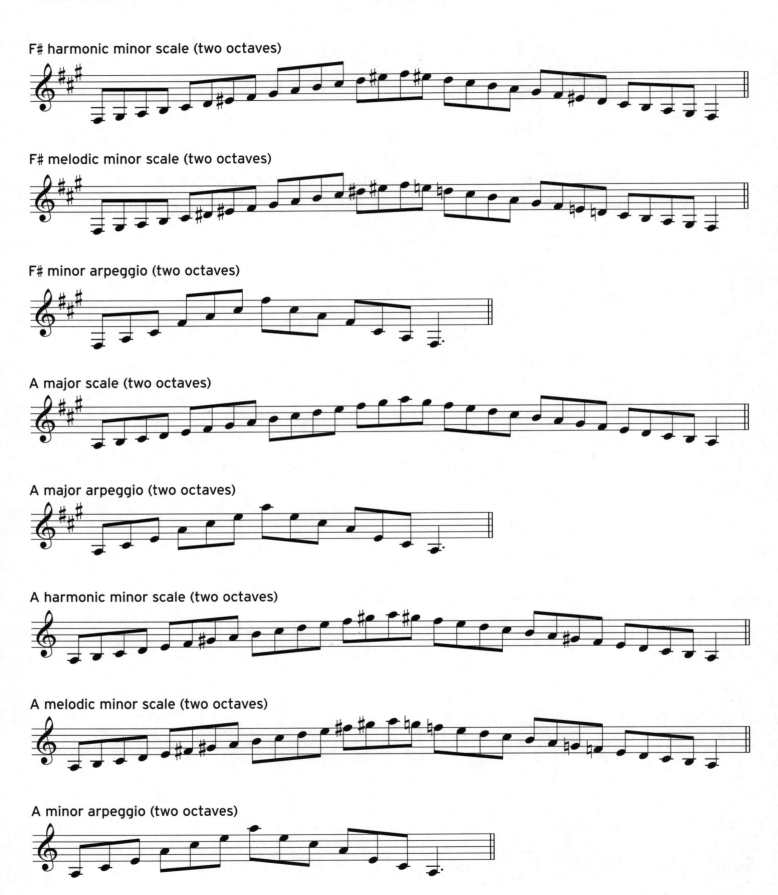

Chromatic scale starting on A (two octaves)

Whole-tone scale starting on A (two octaves)

Augmented arpeggio starting on A (two octaves)

Dominant 7th in the key of A (one octave)*

Diminished 7th starting on A (two octaves)

*If preferred, the dominant 7th may be finished on the starting note rather than resolving onto the tonic.

Grade 6 continued

or ii) **Exercises:**

The following exercises to be performed *either* tongued *or* including slurs as indicated, as requested by the examiner
(♩ = 72–120):

Key centre exercise in A

A major expanding scale exercise

A minor expanding scale exercise

A major scale in thirds

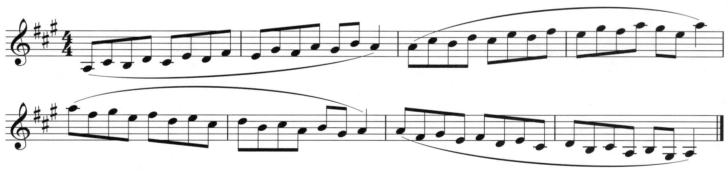

A minor scale in thirds

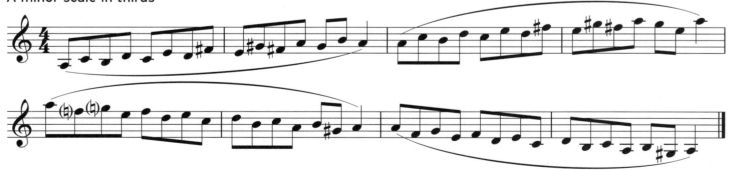

Grade 7

Candidate to prepare one lip flexibility exercise and then *either* Section i) *or* Section ii) in full:

Lip Flexibility Exercise:

No. 1 Ascending

♩ = *c.* 160   Play this exercise slurred, using the valve combinations given.

Repeat using the following valve combinations:

2nd and 3rd - 1st and 2nd - 1st - 2nd

or

No. 2 Descending

♩ = *c.* 92   Play this exercise slurred, using the valve combinations given.

Repeat using the following valve combinations:

2nd - 1st - 1st and 2nd - 2nd and 3rd - 1st and 3rd

either i) **Scales and Arpeggios (from memory):**

The following scales and arpeggios to be performed $\boldsymbol{f}$ or $\boldsymbol{p}$, tongued *or* slurred *or* staccato tongued as requested by the examiner ($\quarternote$ = 80-126):

B♭ major scale (two octaves)

B♭ major arpeggio (two octaves)

B♭ harmonic minor scale (two octaves)

B♭ melodic minor scale (two octaves)

B♭ minor arpeggio (two octaves)

Chromatic scale starting on B♭ (two octaves)

Whole-tone scale starting on B♭ (two octaves)

Grade 7 continued

Augmented arpeggio starting on B♭ (two octaves)

Dominant 7th in the key of B♭ (one octave)*

Diminished 7th starting on B♭ (two octaves)

B major scale (two octaves)

B major arpeggio (two octaves)

B harmonic minor scale (two octaves)

B melodic minor scale (two octaves)

B minor arpeggio (two octaves)

*If preferred, the dominant 7th may be finished on the starting note rather than resolving onto the tonic.

Chromatic scale starting on B (two octaves)

Whole-tone scale starting on B (two octaves)

Augmented arpeggio starting on B (two octaves)

Dominant 7th in the key of B (one octave)*

Diminished 7th starting on B (two octaves)

*If preferred, the dominant 7th may be finished on the starting note rather than resolving onto the tonic.

Grade 7 continued

or ii) **Exercises:**

The following exercises to be performed *either* tongued *or* including slurs as indicated, as requested by the examiner (♩ = 80-126):

Key centre exercise in B♭

B♭ major expanding scale exercise

B♭ minor scale in thirds

B major scale in thirds

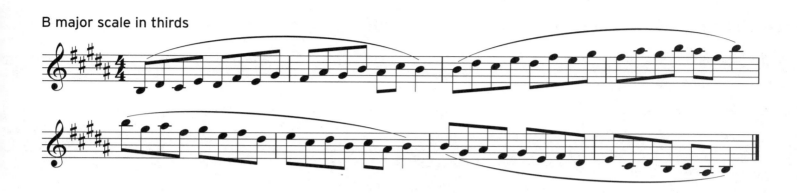

B minor expanding scale exercise

Grade 8

Candidate to prepare one lip flexibility exercise and then *either* Section i) *or* Section ii) in full:

Lip Flexibility Exercise:

No. 1 Ascending

♩ = *c.* 92   Play this exercise slurred, using the valve combinations given.

Repeat using the following valve combinations:

2nd and 3rd - 1st and 2nd - 1st - 2nd - open

or

No. 2 Descending

♩ = *c.* 92   Play this exercise slurred, using the valve combinations given.

Repeat using the following valve combinations:

2nd - 1st - 1st and 2nd - 2nd and 3rd - 1st and 3rd

either i) **Scales and Arpeggios (from memory):**

The following scales and arpeggios to be performed *f* or *p*, tongued *or* slurred *or* staccato tongued *or* slurred in pairs (scales only) as requested by the examiner. ♩ = 88–132

C major scale (two octaves)

C major arpeggio (two octaves)

C harmonic minor scale (two octaves)

C melodic minor scale (two octaves)

C minor arpeggio (two octaves)

Chromatic scale starting on C (two octaves)

Whole-tone scale starting on C (two octaves)

Augmented arpeggio starting on C (two octaves)

Dominant 7th in the key of C (two octaves)*

*If preferred, the dominant 7th may be finished on the starting note rather than resolving onto the tonic.

Grade 8 continued

Diminished 7th starting on C (two octaves)

F# major scale (two octaves)

F# major arpeggio (two octaves)

F# harmonic minor scale (two octaves)

F# melodic minor scale (two octaves)

F# minor arpeggio (two octaves)

Chromatic scale starting on F# (two octaves)

Whole-tone scale starting on F# (two octaves)

Augmented arpeggio starting on F# (two octaves)

Dominant 7th in the key of F# (one octave)*

Diminished 7th starting on F# (two octaves)

A♭ major scale (two octaves)

A♭ major arpeggio (two octaves)

G#/A♭ harmonic minor scale (two octaves)

*If preferred, the dominant 7th may be finished on the starting note rather than resolving onto the tonic.

Grade 8 continued

G#/A♭ melodic minor scale (two octaves)

G#/A♭ minor arpeggio (two octaves)

Chromatic scale starting on A♭ (two octaves)

Whole-tone scale starting on A♭ (two octaves)

Augmented arpeggio starting on A♭ (two octaves)

Dominant 7th in the key of A♭ (one octave)*

Diminished 7th starting on G#/A♭ (two octaves)

*If preferred, the dominant 7th may be finished on the starting note rather than resolving onto the tonic.

Crabwise scale from C (two octaves - tongued *or* slurred as indicated)

Crabwise scale from G (two octaves - tongued *or* slurred as indicated)

Grade 8 continued

or ii) **Exercises:**

The following exercises to be performed *either* tongued *or* including slurs as indicated, as requested by the examiner
(♩ = 88-132):

Key centre exercise in C

Key centre exercise in F♯

Key centre exercise in A♭

Crabwise scale from G in thirds